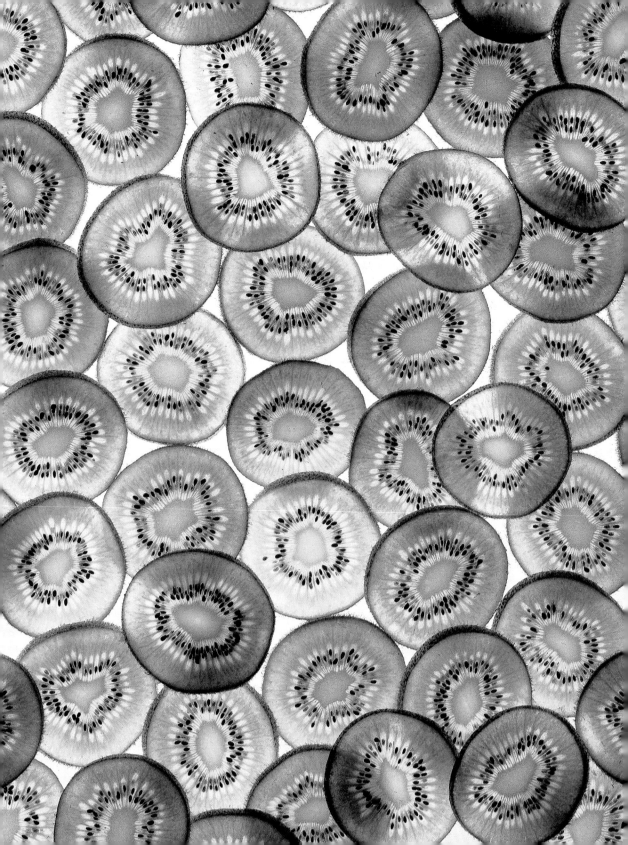

Ashton Scholastic acknowledges the invaluable assistance
of the New Zealand Kiwifruit Marketing Board
and Kiwifruit Country New Zealand
in the production of this book.

First published 1990

Ashton Scholastic Limited
Private Bag 1, Penrose, Auckland 5, New Zealand.

Ashton Scholastic Pty Ltd
PO Box 579, Gosford, NSW 2250, Australia.

Scholastic Inc.
730 Broadway, New York, NY 10003, USA.

Scholastic-TAB Publications Ltd
123 Newkirk Road, Richmond Hill, Ontario L4C 3G5, Canada.

Scholastic Publications Ltd
Marlborough House, Holly Walk, Leamington Spa, Warwickshire CV32 4LS, England.

Text copyright © John Parker, 1989
Photographs pages 3, 5, 7, 17 & 19 by Bob Tulloch
Photographs pages 21, 23, 25 & 27 by Visual Art Studios
Photographs pages 9, 11, 13 & 15 supplied by NZ Kiwifruit Marketing Board

National Library of New Zealand
Cataloguing-in-Publication data

Parker, John.
  Journey : the kiwifruit story / by John Parker. Auckland N.Z. :
Ashton Scholastic, 1990.
    1 v. (Read by reading)
    Reader for children.
    Life of kiwifruit from planting to eating.
    ISBN 0-908643-93-4
    1. Readers — Kiwifruit. I. Title. II. Series: Read by reading series
    428.6 (634.4)

54321   01234/9

Designed by Julie Roil
Typeset in Novarese by Rennies Illustrations
Printed in Hong Kong

JOURNEY
THE KIWIFRUIT STORY

JOHN PARKER

READ BY READING

Ashton Scholastic
Auckland   Sydney   New York   Toronto   London

The farmer
planted them,

the rain
watered them,

the netting
sheltered them,

the tester
checked them,

the harvester
picked them,

the grader
selected them,

the packer
boxed them,

the driver
delivered them,

  the auctioneer
extolled them,

the shopkeeper
displayed them,

the customers
admired them,

but my mother
bought them . . .

24

  and I ate them!

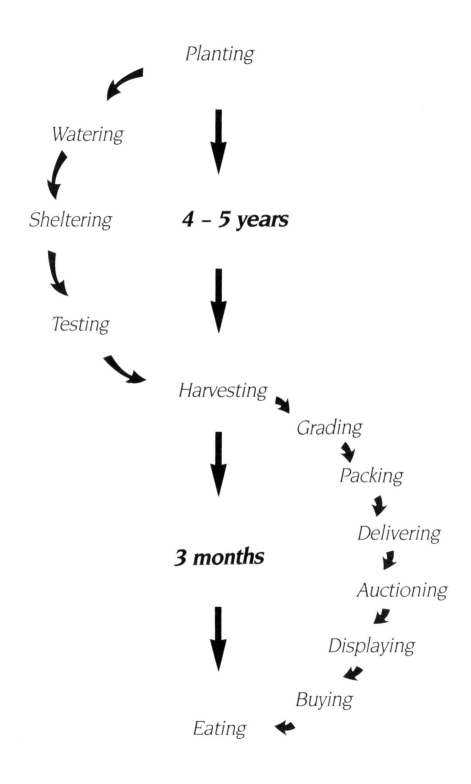

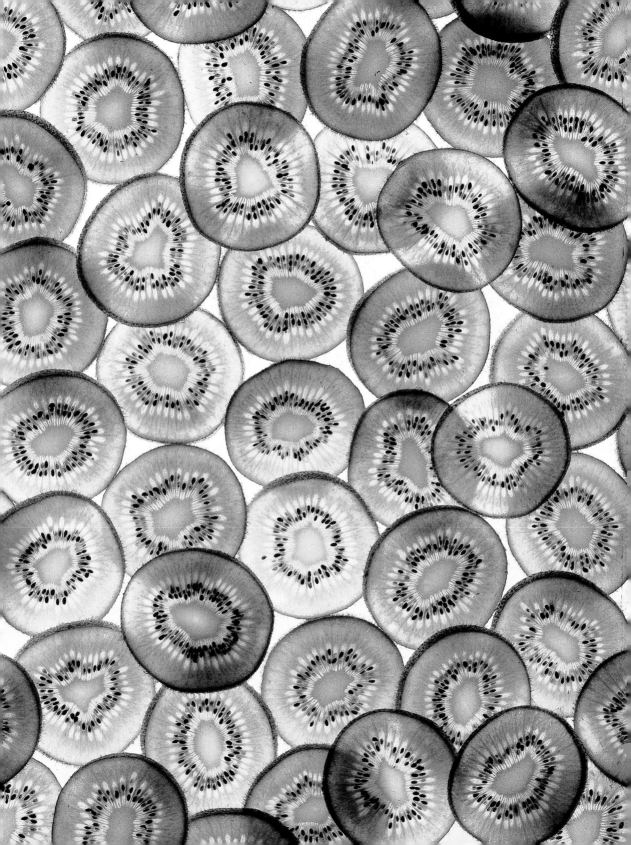